CONTENTS

P9-BZI-344

On your mark, get set, go! The puzzles in this level are designed to get your brain in gear.

Things start to get a little trickier here. Power through!

The puzzles here are the toughest of the bunch. Are you up to the challenge?

Get Ready for Fun and Games!

Look no further, kids! *Brain Games™ Kids: Puzzle Blast!* is here, and it's jam-packed with brainteasers that will pump up your puzzle power and provide the fun. You'll find twisty mazes, illustrated puzzles, word riddles, and many more.

We've put our heads together to come up with a big-time collection of puzzles and loaded them into this handy, pocket-size book. Your favorite teasers are sorted into levels, so you can kick off with an easy one in the first level or fast-track straight to the toughest challenges

in Level 3. Skip around and work a variety of puzzles—you'll have fun for days, and your mind will get the workout it needs!

Another thing to keep in mind is that every answer is included in the back of the book. You want to be sure to give each puzzle a try, but the solutions are there to get you back on track in case you get stuck.

Kids, now you're ready to get moving! So grab a pencil, and get your noggin cooking with *Brain Games™ Kids: Puzzle Blast!*

Parent's note: The more than 100 kid-friendly brainteasers in *Brain Games™ Kids: Puzzle Blast!* will hold your child's interest for hours while also giving their brains a boost and improving their language skills, analytic thinking, and logical reasoning.

Compact and portable, this book can go everywhere your kids go—school, dance class, soccer practice, or a visit to the dentist's office. (It might even make the trip to a teeth scrubbing a little more fun!) So give them this book, and turn them loose on puzzling!

BEGIN WITH A BANG

Face Off

Can you spot the 2 identical faces?

Answer on page 125.

Word Math

This puzzle works exactly like a regular math problem, but instead of using numbers in the equation you use letters. First, fill in the blanks with the name for each picture. Then solve the equation.

_ _ _ _   _ _ _ _   _ _ _

Word Ladder

Change just one letter on each line to go from the top word to the bottom word. Do not change the order of the letters. You must have a common English word at each step.

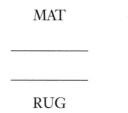

MAT

_____

_____

RUG

 Answers on page 125.

Decoder

· ·

Unscramble the letters below to reveal the answer to this question: I am light as a feather, yet the strongest man can't hold me for long. What am I?

B R E A T H

Answer on page 125.

Pic-doku

The grid below is divided into 4 sections. Your job is to have each of the 4 items appear once in each section and in each row and column. Fill each square with the item's image or the letter that represents it. No item can repeat in any section, row, or column.

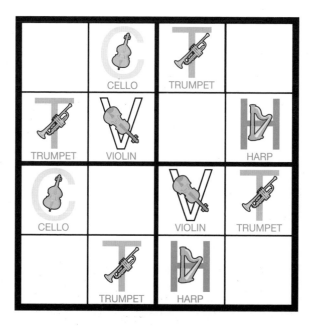

Answer on page 125.

Kids' Games

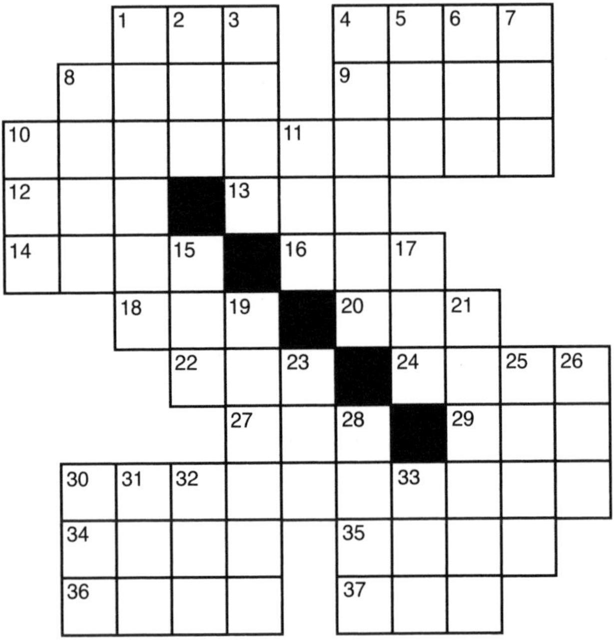

ACROSS

1. Angry
4. The alphabet
8. Red flower
9. Songbird that's a symbol of happiness
10. Game of polite questions: 3 wds.
12. Flowery poem
13. Twosome
14. It holds up your pants
16. Come to a finish
18. Drink slowly
20. Homer Simpson, to Bart
22. Bit of butter
24. Spread it on a sandwich: abbr.

27. Become spoiled
29. Just purchased
30. Kids' yard game: 3 wds.
34. It comes from your brain
35. "They lived happily _____ after"
36. Five are on each foot
37. "That's right!"

DOWN

1. Tourists stay in them
2. Remains of burnt paper
3. A scout may do a good one
4. Candy bar nut
5. Sound of a sheep
6. Shed tears
7. Slide down a white slope
8. Went on a horse
10. Angry crowd
11. Regret (hidden in "gruel")
15. Money on the restaurant table
17. Barrier built by beavers
19. Winter jackets
21. Does the tango or twist
23. Small child
25. 12 months
26. Possess
28. "If _____ could see me now"
30. Box full of model airplane parts, for example
31. Two words said at a wedding
32. Letter after bee
33. Night before Christmas

Dozen Pawprints Blots

Two of the blots below are identical in shape and color. Can you find them?

12　　　Answer on page 125.

Silly Sundae Shop

There are 16 things that don't belong in this picture.
Can you spot them all?

Answers on page 126.

Picture-by-Number

Shade in the numbers that are divisible by 4. Once complete, the grid will reveal a simple image.

1	79	67	48	2	95	93	34
22	21	91	96	31	74	14	47
95	14	100	24	64	73	41	34
47	61	45	36	87	75	73	62
7	88	40	80	8	28	75	75
63	55	27	80	65	29	97	81
72	88	36	12	60	36	20	9
81	57	92	12	92	51	6	13

Tentacles!

It's trouble in the sea! Help the little fish escape the octopus.

Answer on page 126.

Crosspic

Looks like someone put pictures in this puzzle where there are supposed to be words! See if you can fill in the grid by writing the word—one letter for each box—that names each of the pictures. Words run across and down.

16   Answers on page 126.

Picture Crossword

Look at the pictures on this page, and name each one. Then write the word in the correct numbered spaces. Be sure to check to see if the word should be written across or down.

ACROSS

1.

3.

5.

6.

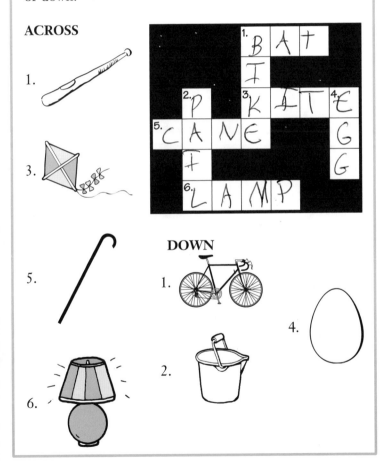

DOWN

1.

2.

4.

17   Answers on page 126.

A Bug's Life

Can you find all the creepy crawlies pictured below listed in the grid? Words can be found in a straight line horizontally, vertically, or diagonally. They may be read either forward or backward.

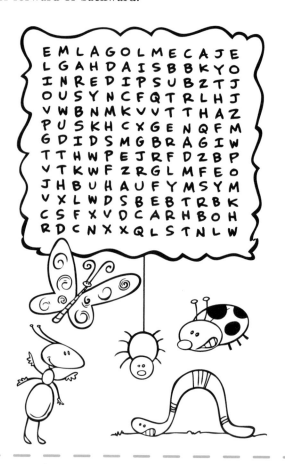

```
E M L A G O L M E C A J E
L G A H D A I S B B K Y O
I N R E D I P S U B Z T J
O U S Y N C F Q T R L H J
V W B N M K V V T T H A Z
P U S K H C X G E N Q F M
G D I D S M G B R A G I W
T T H W P E J R F D Z B P
V T K W F Z R G L M F E O
J H B U H A U F Y M S Y M
V X L W D S B E B T R B K
C S F X V D C A R H B O H
R D C N X X Q L S T N L W
```

Answers on page 127.

Flippy Numbers

Below is an incorrect equation. Can you swap 2 of the number cards to get a correct equation?

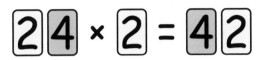

Black Diamonds

Place the numbers 1 through 4 in the cells of each of the squares below. There's a catch though: Overlapping cells must add up to the number given in the black diamond.

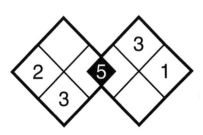

Answers on page 127.

K Is for Kite

Looks like a perfect day to fly a kite! It's also a perfect setting for objects beginning with the letter **K.** Can you find all 20?

20   Answers on page 127.

Crosspic

Looks like someone put pictures in this puzzle where there are supposed to be words! See if you can fill in the grid by writing the word—one letter for each box—that names each of the pictures. Words run across and down.

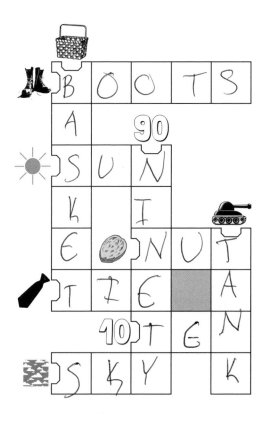

Answers on page 127.

Jungle Tree

Can you spot all 10 differences between these safari scenes?

23 Answers on page 127.

Clowning Around at the Circus

Check out all of the attractions at the circus, but don't get lost as you make your way from start to finish!

24

Answer on page 128.

Birthday Party!

Yesterday was Ryan's birthday, and his parents celebrated by throwing him a party! Most of the guests were family members, but Ryan was able to invite his friends as well. Ryan played games, received presents, and ate birthday cake and ice cream. Can you determine the name of each of Ryan's friends, the gift they gave Ryan, and the flavor of ice cream they ate?

1. Matt's present was a music CD, but he didn't have vanilla ice cream.

2. Joe had chocolate ice cream, but he didn't give Ryan a movie.

3. Elliot didn't have mocha chip ice cream, but his present was a video game.

4. George had strawberry ice cream, but he didn't give Ryan a book.

Name	Gift	Flavor
Matt	CD	chocolate

Answers on page 128.

A Change of Seasons

Find the 3 objects that appear in both seasonal scenes!

Answers on page 128.

Bug Off!

Every word listed is contained within the group of letters below. Words can be found in a straight line horizontally, vertically, or diagonally. They may be read either forward or backward.

CHINCH
CROTON
DOODLE
FIRE
GOLD
JITTER
JUNE
LADY
LIGHTNING
LITTER
LOVE
MEALY
POTATO
SHUTTER
STINK

```
R  E  T  T  I  L  O  D  N  Q
M  E  A  L  Y  R  S  Y  A  H
X  S  T  N  O  T  O  R  C  D
I  T  P  T  S  J  E  N  L  S
U  I  W  O  U  T  I  O  D  F
G  N  I  N  T  H  G  I  L  G
Q  K  E  I  C  A  S  E  D  P
Y  H  J  G  W  O  T  V  S  T
F  I  R  E  L  D  O  O  D  O
K  G  F  T  Y  D  A  L  A  G
```

Answers on page 128.

Nine Mushroom Blots

Two of the blots below are identical in shape and color. Can you find them?

Answer on page 128.

Color Challenge

Place the following colors into the grid so that they intersect as in a crossword. When you are done, all the words will have been used exactly once. We filled in the first one for you.

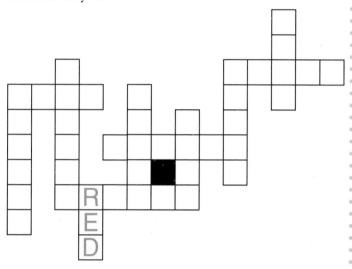

3 Letters

red

4 Letters

blue

gray

pink

5 Letters

black

brown

green

6 Letters

indigo

orange

purple

yellow

Answers on page 129.

A Day at the Zoo

Help Jilly and Jeffrey find their way through the zoo. Feel free to stop and visit with some animal friends on the way!

EXIT

Answer on page 129

Monster Mash-Up!

There are 5 things out of place at this hoppin' Halloween party, and it's up to you to find them all!

31   Answers on page 129.

Awesome Animals

Can you identify each of these animals just by the sounds that they make? Then, find those animals in the grid. Words can be found in a straight line vertically or diagonally. They may be read either forward or backward. We gave you the first letter of each animal.

1. TRUMPET

    E _ _ _ _ _ _ _

2. HISS

    S _ _ _ _

3. HEE-HAW, HEE-HAW

    D _ _ _ _ _

4. GOBBLE, GOBBLE

    T _ _ _ _ _

5. ROAR

    L _ _ _

6. BAA, BAA

    S _ _ _ _

7. COCK-A-DOODLE-DOOOOO!

    R _ _ _ _ _ _

8. HOWL

    W _ _ _

9. SQUAWK!

P _ _ _ _ _

10. NEIGH

H _ _ _ _

11. RIBBIT, RIBBIT

F _ _ _

12. QUACK

D _ _ _

```
M X O P G T T M Q V T K L E H
F R C P O R M G F C C Y M J N
E O X R K D L Q T S A D O R J
Y G R U G K L M V U Z O P W U
L A S S Q C S E L O R N J Y A
P Z N Q W U Q E S F N K S T B
M Z A R R D Z J T D M E E E H
R Q K T S E S N P L B Y S Y S
O P E L U T A M C P H X R O L
O D M R F H A X I Y E K O Y A
S T X L P D M V U E D E H Q F
T V O E Q K T Z Z F N W H A L
E W L G S Q Z L R O N F C S L
R E G C X Q B O I J C O N Q F
L A F Q T J G L W M H K O Y Q
```

Chain Words

Place 2 letters in the middle squares that will complete one word and start another. For example, ER would complete FLI - ER - ROR.

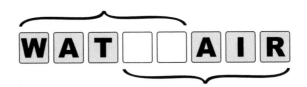

Word Math

This puzzle works exactly like a regular math problem, but instead of using numbers in the equation you use letters. First, fill in the blanks with the name for each picture. Then solve the equation.

Graveyard Shuffle

You're going to have to dig your way out of this maze!

 Answer on page 130.

Family Ties

Divide the grid into 4 sections with each section containing 4 squares. Every section must contain one of each of the family members—mother, father, brother, and sister.

Hint: Look for places where the same family member is bunched together, and start there.

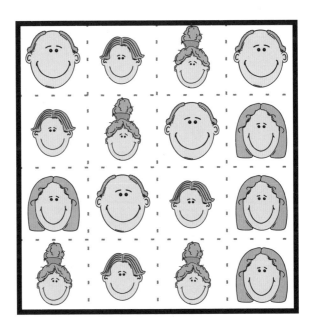

Answer on page 130.

Picture-by-Number

Shade in the numbers that are divisible by 6. Once complete, the grid will reveal a simple image.

189	33	90	52	77	173	79	54	89	38
122	174	162	192	96	42	84	174	114	182
53	72	72	142	66	144	92	12	96	7
4	42	30	156	168	84	108	114	96	71
134	48	11	60	132	54	54	2	108	157
158	180	156	197	111	110	23	192	12	127
62	91	174	60	54	108	126	198	5	29
152	152	163	81	30	168	178	196	171	101
137	116	25	31	96	54	60	113	147	68
141	101	99	103	174	12	162	156	48	51

Answer on page 130.

Big Top!

Every word listed is contained within the group of letters on the next page. Words can be found in a straight line horizontally, vertically, or diagonally. They may be read either forward or backward.

BARKER

BARNUM AND
  BAILEY

CARNEY

CLOWNS

CONTORTIONIST

COTTON CANDY

ELEPHANT

FERRIS WHEEL

FIRE-EATER

JUGGLER

MIDWAY

PITCHMAN

RINGLING BROS.

RINGMASTER

SIDESHOW

SWORD
  SWALLOWER

TENT

THREE RINGS

TIGER

TIGHTROPE

TRAPEZE

TUMBLER

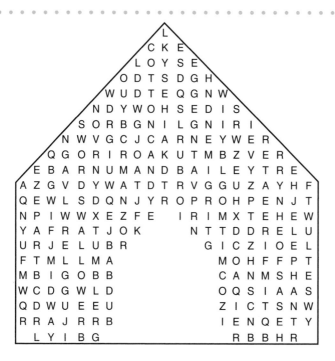

```
              L
            C K E
          L O Y S E
        O D T S D G H
      W U D T E Q G N W
    N D Y W O H S E D I S
    S O R B G N I L G N I R I
  N W V G C J C A R N E Y W E R
  Q G O R I R O A K U T M B Z V E R
 E B A R N U M A N D B A I L E Y T R E
A Z G V D Y W A T D T R V G G U Z A Y H F
Q E W L S D Q N J Y R O P R O H P E N J T
N P I W W X E Z F E   I R I M X T E H E W
Y A F R A T J O K     N T T D D R E L U
U R J E L U B R       G I C Z I O E L
F T M L L M A         M O H F F P T
M B I G O B B         C A N M S H E
W C D G W L D         O Q S I A A S
Q D W U E E U         Z I C T S N W
R R A J R R B         I E N Q E T Y
 L Y I B G            R B B H R
```

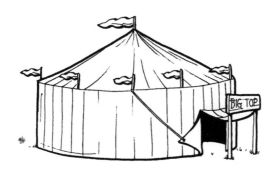

Answers on page 130.

Space Hop

Get the spaceship to the star at the top right corner of the page by moving through alternating shapes. You can move either horizontally or vertically.

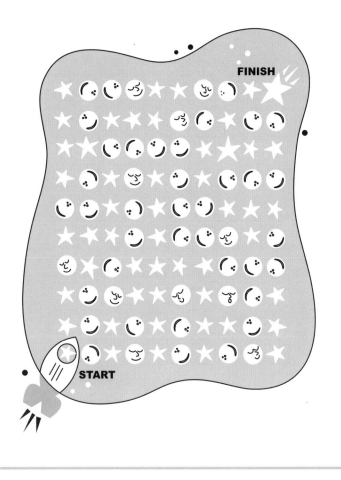

FINISH

START

40

Answer on page 130.

Pic-doku

The grid below is divided into 4 sections. Your job is to have each of the 4 items appear once in each section and in each row and column. Fill each square with the item's image or the letter that represents it. No item can repeat in any section, row, or column.

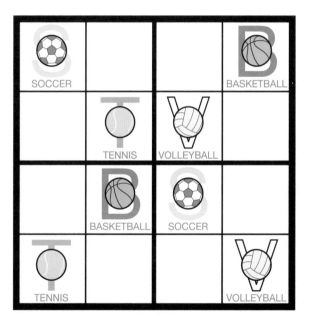

Summertime

There's no time to relax when there are 6 things wrong with this beach scene! Can you find them all?

Answers on page 131.

Crosspic

Looks like someone put pictures in this puzzle where there are supposed to be words! See if you can fill in the grid by writing the word—one letter for each box—that names each of the pictures. Words run across and down.

Answers on page 131.

POWER THROUGH

Vex-a-Gon

Place the numbers 1 through 6 into the triangles of each hexagon. The numbers may be in any order, but they do not repeat within each hexagon shape.

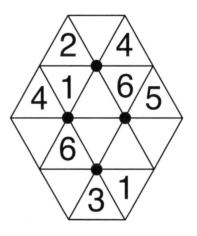

Cat Burglar

The sneaky cat is looking for a free meal. Get him through the vent so he can sneak off with the catch of the day!

45   Answer on page 131.

Pic-doku

The grid below is divided into 4 sections. Your job is to have each of the 4 items appear once in each section and in each row and column. Fill each square with the item's image or the letter that represents it. No item can repeat in any section, row, or column.

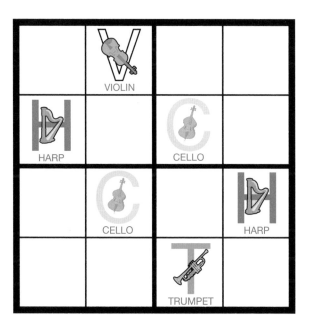

Answer on page 131.

Riddle in the Middle

Use the clues to complete the 5-letter answers, starting at the top and working your way down. When finished, read the letters in the squares with the thick boxes, from top to bottom, to reveal the answer to the riddle below.

What goes through a door but never goes in or out?

1. Foot joint

A [ ] [ ] E

2. Coffee extra

C [ ] [ ] M

3. Faithful

L [ ] [ ] L

4. Remains of a fire

A [ ] [ ] S

5. Soup utensil

S [ ] [ ] N

6. Goofy

S [ ] [ ] Y

7. What becomes toast

B [ ] [ ] D

47   Answers on page 132.

Flower Bed

How many different kind of flowers are there? Which flower appears the most? Which flower appears only once?

Answers on page 132.

Crosspic

Looks like someone put pictures in this puzzle where there are supposed to be words! See if you can fill in the grid by writing the word—one letter for each box—that names each of the pictures. Words run across and down.

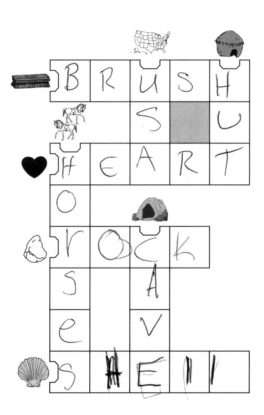

Answers on page 132.

Find the Differences

• •

Race to find all 10 changes between these pictures. On your mark, get set, GO!

51   Answers on page 132.

Flippy Numbers

Below is an incorrect equation. Can you swap 2 of the number cards to get a correct equation?

$$\boxed{3}\boxed{9} \div \boxed{3} = \boxed{3}\boxed{9}$$

Word Ladder

Change just one letter on each line to go from the top word to the bottom word. Do not change the order of the letters. You must have a common English word at each step.

LOST

_____

_____

_____

COIN

Answers on page 132.

Dozen Fish Blots

Two of the blots below are identical in shape and color. Can you find them?

Answer on page 132.

Petting Zoo

ACROSS

1. "All in favor, say
   _____"
4. Said "not guilty," for
   example
8. Pea container
9. Like energy from the
   sun
10. Use them to look
12. Spin like a top
13. Animals with long ears
    and long tails
15. Cry like a kitty
16. "Now _____ seen
    everything!"
17. Male adult
18. Letter before dee
19. Possesses
20. Ticked off
21. Purchase
22. Smash into
23. Animals with long ears
    and cottontails
27. Unlocked
29. Sound that bounces
30. Boy's name (found in
    "challenge")
31. Snaky fish
32. Take a break
33. Take notice of

DOWN

1. Imitated
2. Toy on a string
3. Biblical garden
4. Flower holder
5. Pack animals of Peru
6. Gobbled down
7. Made pictures
9. Sinking ship's signal
11. Slid on the snow
12. Kind of bread
14. Adam's wife
17. Perhaps
18. Animals of the desert
19. Wheel's center
20. Tree that gives sap for
    syrup
21. Naughty
22. Sound from "The Lion
    King"
23. Stimpy's pal
24. Covers a cupcake
25. You, in the Bible
26. Boot bottom
28. Volleyball court divider

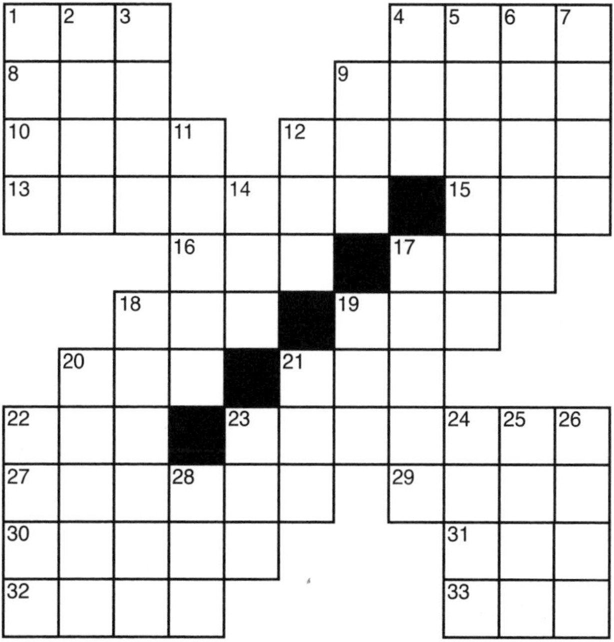

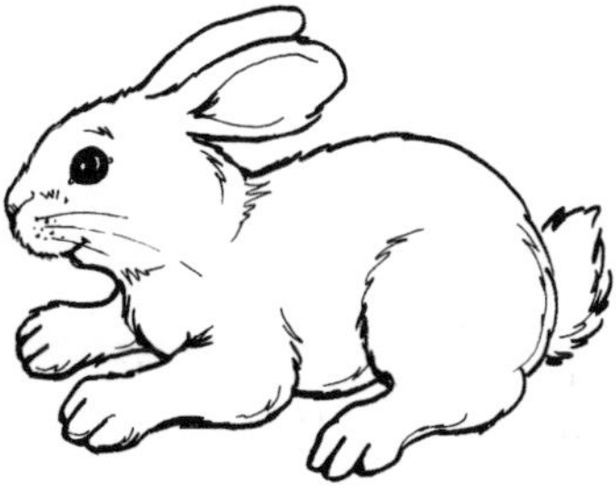

 Answers on page 133.

The Best Medicine

You'll want to take this one with a spoonful of sugar!
Words can be found in a straight line horizontally,
vertically, or diagonally. They may be read either
forward or backward.

CACKLE
CHEER
CHORTLE
CHUCKLE
CRACK UP
CROW
GIGGLE
GLEE
GRIN

GUFFAW
HAPPINESS
HILARITY
HOOT
HOWL
JOVIAL
JOY
LAUGHTER
MERRIMENT

MIRTH
PEAL
ROAR
SNICKER
SNORT
WHOOP
YUCK

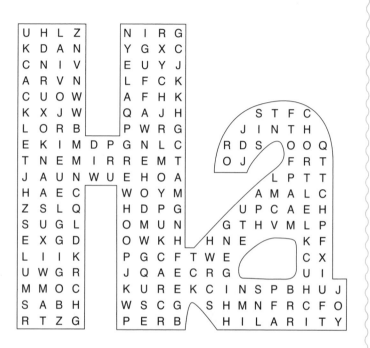

Answers on page 133.

Animal Band

Rock this scene by finding 8 hidden things!

BELL   FLASHLIGHT   PENCIL

CANDLE   KEY   SNAKE

DOMINO   NEEDLE

58   Answers on page 133.

Snake Tangle

Which tail belongs to which snake?

 Answers on page 133.

Face Off

Can you spot the 2 identical faces?

Answer on page 133.

Library Mix-Up

There are 19 things wrong with this picture. Can you spot them all?

Answers on page 134.

Dog Breeds

Every word listed is contained within the group of letters on the next page. Words can be found in a straight line horizontally, vertically, or diagonally. They may be read either forward or backward.

AIREDALE

BEAGLE

BEDLINGTON

BLENHEIM

BOXER

CAIRN

CHOW

COCKER SPANIEL

COLLIE

CORGI

GREYHOUND

HUSKY

IRISH SETTER

PAPILLON

POINTER

POODLE

PUG

SALUKI

SAMOYED

SPITZ

WHIPPET

```
        C  O
       H Z  A Z B
      O O   L L T J I
     W Z D   E K O I E Z O
   F H A     N O L L I P A P
   P I        H I K U L A S S
   C P Z X O F  E U P Q L Q
   I P T D E Y O M A S M N V K C O A K
   L E I N A P S R E K C O C Y O I J F
   T D U I R I S H S E T T E R H C
   G O R E T N I O P G Y N G B
   O H E X P G P U G N B C I
   H Y D O G    O Q I E I
     E A B      O L A E
     R L        D G
     G E W X    E L Z S
     P H Y M    B E E O
```

Disney Toons

ACROSS

1. Hereditary unit
5. Owned
8. Mideast native
9. Raw metals
11. "The Lion King" character
13. "Beauty and the Beast" character
15. "_____ haw" (donkey sound)
16. Close relative of sis
18. Bathtub submarine, e.g.
19. Event for bargain hunters
21. Fence opening
22. "Aladdin" character

24. Like an overdue book
27. Adam and Eve's first home
29. State next to Miss.
30. Golf ball peg
31. Have unpaid bills
34. Disney film title that is a deer character
36. "The Little Mermaid" character
38. Can't do without
39. Puts to work
40. Barely passing grade, like Cee
41. Work at the keyboard

DOWN
1. Deep cut
2. One of the Great Lakes
3. Tom, Dick, and Harry
4. Go out, on the beach
5. Wanderer
6. "There you _____!"
7. Mouth of a river, often
10. Piggy bank opening
12. Up to the task
14. You use it to see
17. Girl's name (hidden in "dire need")
20. Get older
21. "Golly!"
23. Thought
24. Dog, or work area
25. Boy's name (hidden in "balance")
26. Like animals that are safe to pet
28. Like a room full of talking kids
30. It goes out on the beach
32. Shed tears
33. "So, what _____ is new?"
35. Honey-making insect
37. Wheel track

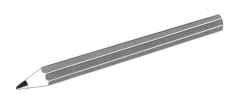

65

Answers on page 134.

F Is for Favorites

We found 13 objects in this picture starting with the letter **F**. How many can you find?

Answers on page 134.

Telescope

Enter the names of the pictures into the telescope so each word overlaps one or more words. For example, if the words were BOW, OWL, LEMON, and ONION, the chain of letters would be BOWLEMONION. However, the pictures are in random order below.

67   Answer on page 134.

Save the Mayor

A monster has attacked the city, and this superhero is the only one who can save the mayor. Make your way through the maze and release the mayor from the monster's grip.

Answer on page 135.

Cake Connection

Which 2 cakes from Pierre's Pattiseries are exactly the same?

Answer on page 135.

School Day

Every word listed is contained within the group of letters on the next page. Words can be found in a straight line horizontally, vertically, or diagonally. They may be read either forward or backward.

BELL	MATH
BOOK	MUSIC
CHAIR	NOTES
CHART	NURSE
CLOCK	PAGE
CRAYON	PENCIL
DESK	SCHOOL
ENGLISH	SHELF
ERASER	SINK
FILM	SOCIAL STUDIES
FLOOR	SPANISH
GLUE	TABLE
GYMNASTICS	TAPE
HALL	TRASH
LIGHT	WALL

```
R I A H C P B R R V C S M K U
G N J O G R E K X D N E M G W
S O E U E S J P E N C I L G L
G Y M N A S T I C S E D I D N
G A K R G N F L E H S U F M Y
Y R E D S L Y E L B A T L U P
E C E N E H I L L E B S M G W
U S Q A T S N S G T L L A W V
K P Y M O A S A H E P A T Q Q
K A U K N R P C S P K I H H R
D N I U V T H T H R F C B A T
B I R M U S I C H O N O O L R
B S T N Q R I L D G O S O L O
E H T R A H C N Z G I L K X C
I F F I U F T B K F F L O O R
```

 Answers on page 135.

Picture-by-Number

Shade in the numbers that are divisible by 3. Once complete, the grid will reveal a simple image.

56	20	72	93	25	16	40	89	45	39	65	71
17	93	43	7	43	41	88	62	14	19	6	32
10	92	40	81	58	77	95	67	87	37	95	74
52	22	3	34	63	89	80	54	73	24	41	58
56	85	92	21	47	89	49	86	63	71	73	52
26	44	46	56	14	87	27	77	98	40	89	23
5	96	20	2	54	81	48	45	89	50	30	89
19	60	25	29	38	84	39	43	20	49	21	35
17	79	42	26	64	86	59	47	65	78	80	34
55	44	73	75	51	69	27	30	24	50	47	38
32	73	4	24	86	85	65	62	48	77	14	98
31	35	37	67	90	57	96	27	91	2	47	7

Answer on page 135.

Crosspic

Looks like someone put pictures in this puzzle where there are supposed to be words! See if you can fill in the grid by writing the word—one letter for each box—that names each of the pictures. Words run across and down.

73 Answers on page 135.

Bonnie's Birthday Bash!

There are 11 everyday objects (listed below) hidden in this celebration scene. Join the party and find them all!

CRESCENT MOON

ENVELOPE

FEATHER

FLASHLIGHT

FRIED EGG

GOLF CLUB

KITE

LADLE

LEMON SLICE

PENNANT

SOCK

74

Answers on page 136.

Pasta Party

Wow, that's one big pile of spaghetti! Can you slurp your way through the noodles to make it to the finish?

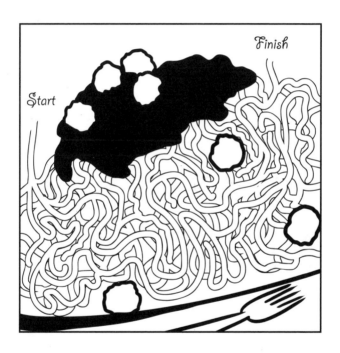

Answer on page 136.

Pic-doku

The grid below is divided into 4 sections. Your job is to have each of the 4 items appear once in each section and in each row and column. Fill each square with the item's image or the letter that represents it. No item can repeat in any section, row, or column.

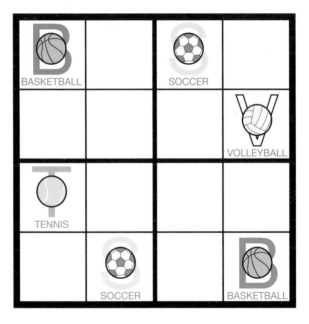

Answer on page 136.

Word Math

This puzzle works exactly like a regular math problem, but instead of using numbers in the equation you use letters. First, fill in the blanks with the name for each picture. Then solve the equation.

___ _____ ___

Flower Growth

Which of these flowers has the longest stem?

Answers on page 136.

Dig It!

If you keep digging, you'll find 10 differences between these pictures easily!

79   Answers on page 136.

Fitting Words

Use the clues below to complete this numberless crossword grid. The puzzle has only one solution.

1. Person performing in a play

2. Chimney dirt

3. You study for them in school

4. This symbol: /

5. Shoestring

6. Picnic-ruining bugs

7. Birch-bark boat

8. Not his

9. "Shoo!"

	L		
			R

Something's Not Right!

There are a few things that aren't quite right with this girl's reflection. Can you spot all 9 differences?

81

Answers on page 137.

Abracadabra!

See if you can perform a trick of your own—finding all the objects on the left in this magical scene!

Answers on page 137.

Damsel in Distress

Free the princess from the tower, but be careful to avoid running into a monster along the way!

83   Answer on page 137.

FINISH WITH FLAIR

Picture-by-Number

Shade in the numbers that are divisible by 7. Once complete, the grid will reveal a simple image.

30	119	49	98	139	118	11	17	126
63	77	126	77	52	3	39	20	42
105	113	84	63	102	97	129	16	105
98	147	147	105	119	84	21	70	140
84	109	84	98	14	42	140	42	18
70	139	63	21	42	133	35	140	79
112	15	134	133	35	140	35	42	48
56	147	85	77	88	87	110	14	89
143	86	121	70	111	146	22	63	24

Pic-doku

The grid below is divided into 4 sections. Your job is to have each of the 4 items appear once in each section and in each row and column. Fill each square with the item's image or the letter that represents it. No item can repeat in any section, row, or column.

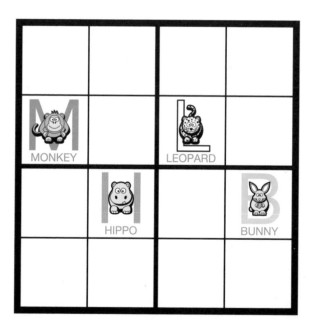

Answer on page 137.

Chain Words

Place 2 letters in the middle squares that will complete one word and start another. For example, ER would complete FLI - ER - ROR.

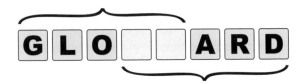

Word Math

This puzzle works exactly like a regular math problem, but instead of using numbers in the equation you use letters. First, fill in the blanks with the name for each picture. Then solve the equation.

Oodles of Octopi

Match the octopus with its exact silhouette below.

 Answer on page 138.

Jumbled Up

Place each letter into the empty boxes below to create a common word. Tiles are in the correct order but they are not in the upright position.

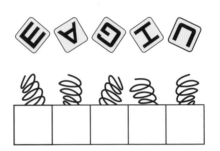

Black Diamonds

Place the numbers 1 through 4 in the cells of each of the squares below. There's a catch though: Overlapping cells must add up to the number given in each of the black diamonds.

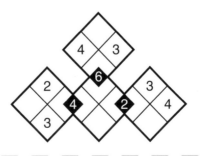

88   Answers on page 138.

Face Off

Can you spot the 2 identical faces?

Answer on page 138.

Circus Animals

ACROSS
1. They're married to pas
4. Girl's name (hidden in "Friday")
7. Throw it at a board
8. Canine circus animals
10. Growling circus animal
11. Boy's name (hidden in "battle royal")
13. "...what a good boy _____"
14. It makes tea cold
16. Particular period in history
17. Cooking instructions
19. Appear to be
20. Barking circus animals
22. Neighborhood
25. My dad's daughter, to me
29. Get married
30. The knee is part of it
31. Abbreviation for a state near Georgia
32. Soup scoop
34. Trotting circus animal
36. Growling circus animal
37. Ocean water in motion

38. Finish
39. Clever

DOWN
1. Art of doing tricks
2. "There you _____!"
3. Zebra marking
4. Not busy
5. She's a deer
6. Have the same opinion
7. 10-cent coin
9. _____ loser
10. Pave roads with it
12. Sweet potato
15. Put an end to
18. "Happiness _____ Warm Puppy"
19. Snake sound
21. They glow on a Christmas tree
22. Tool for punching holes in leather
23. Not fake
24. Boy's name (hidden in "balanced diet")
26. Running late
27. "What _____ can go wrong?"

28. Girl's name (hidden in "Israel")
30. What libraries do with books
33. Boy's name (hidden in "colony")
35. Engine fluid

Answers on page 138.

Bert's Bicycles

Hannah and Holly are looking for identical bikes. Can you spot 2 that are exactly alike?

Answer on page 139.

Alien Invasion!

Each row of aliens (horizontal and vertical) has one thing in common. Find out what it is, and you'll be out of this world! (Hint: You'll be finding six things: One for each row and one for each column.)

Answers on page 139.

Go Fish!

• •

Every word listed is contained within the group of letters on the next page. Words can be found in a straight line horizontally, vertically, or diagonally. They may be read either forward or backward.

BASS	PIKE
BONITO	POMPANO
BULLHEAD	PORGY
CARP	SARDINE
FLOUNDER	SHARK
FLUKE	SKATE
GUPPY	SMELT
HADDOCK	SNOOK
HAMMERHEAD	SOLE
HERRING	STURGEON
MACKEREL	SWORDFISH
MINNOW	TROUT
PERCH	TUNA
PICKEREL	

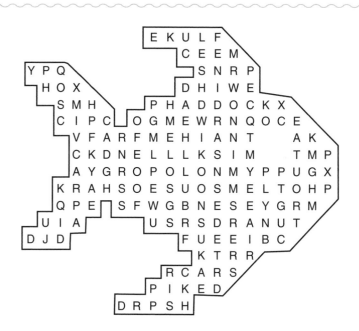

```
              E K U L F
                C E E M
                  S N R P
            D H I W E
    Y P Q        P H A D D O C K X
    H O X      O G M E W R N Q O C E
      S M H  F A R F M E H I A N T     A K
      C I P C K D N E L L L K S I M     T M P
        V A Y G R O P O L O N M Y P P U G X
        C K R A H S O E S U O S M E L T O H P
        A Q P E S F W G B N E S E Y G R M
        K   U S R S D R A N U T
      Q P E   F U E E I B C
    U I A     K T R R
    D J D   R C A R S
          P I K E D
        D R P S H
```

Dozen Stars Blots

Two of the blots below are identical in shape and color.
Can you find them?

96   Answer on page 139.

On the Job

There are 15 objects hidden in this construction scene that start with the letter **T.** Can you find them all?

     Answers on page 139.

Crosspic

Looks like someone put pictures in this puzzle where there are supposed to be words! See if you can fill in the grid by writing the word—one letter for each box—that names each of the pictures. Words run across and down.

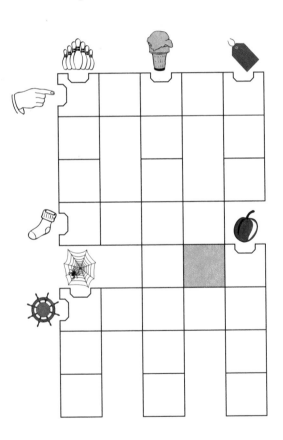

98   Answers on page 140.

Flower Fiesta!

Find your way through the tangled vines to reach the end.

Start

Finish

Answer on page 140.

What You Want on a Picnic

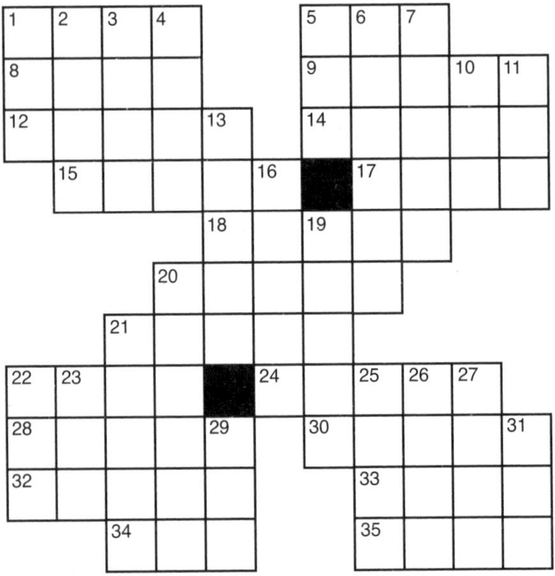

ACROSS

1. You want it on a picnic
5. "Got ya!"
8. In a group of
9. Bottoms of loafers
12. Succotash beans
14. Slanted
15. Musician's speed
17. Disobey
18. Labor group
20. Take with you
21. Get into, as clothes: 2 wds.
22. Many miles away
24. Dressed to the _____
28. "That's it!"
30. Where icicles hang
32. Came to a close
33. Where the light enters the camera

34. "_____ you kidding me?"
35. You don't want them on a picnic

DOWN
1. Boy's name (hidden in "Swiss Alps")
2. Leave out
3. Coin worth 2 nickels
4. Garden of Eden guy
5. Dry _____ bone
6. You want it on a picnic: 2 wds.
7. Visitor from outer space

10. Santa's helper
11. Where pigs stay
13. Sudden gush
16. Bulb fried in rings
19. Bellybutton type
20. You want it on a picnic
21. Bamboo eater
22. President Lincoln, to friends
23. Sign of a shark
25. "The Lion King" lioness
26. Like a tie score
27. Mailed out
29. Poem with lofty words
31. Warning from a snake

Fitting Words

Use the clues below to complete this numberless crossword grid. The puzzle has only one solution.

1. Homes for birds

2. Small brown songbird

3. Use the pink end of a pencil

4. "Woe is me!"

5. Huge ocean mammal

6. They have lenses, irises, and corneas

7. In this spot

8. Final

9. Type of race in which you pass a baton

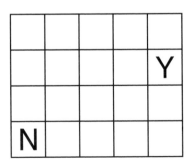

Answer on page 140.

Pic-doku

The grid below is divided into 4 sections. Your job is to have each of the 4 items appear once in each section and in each row and column. Fill each square with the item's image or the letter that represents it. No item can repeat in any section, row, or column.

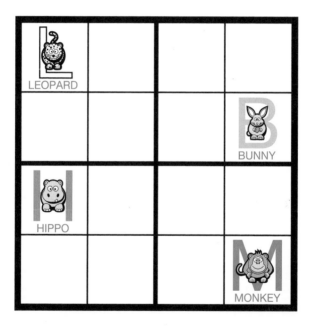

103   Answer on page 140.

Knight-ly Dinner

Something's amiss at this medieval feast; can you spot 8 things that don't belong?

104   Answers on page 141.

Theme Park

This "ride" has a theme, but we can't tell you what it is. Place all the words in the boxes below—when you do, read the word created in the outlined boxes, from top to bottom, to reveal what the theme is.

BRUSH   GLUE   PASTELS

CLAY   MARKER   PENCIL

CRAYONS   PAINT   SCISSORS

EASEL   PAPER

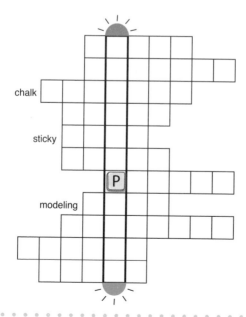

chalk

sticky

P

modeling

105   Answers on page 141.

Great Lesson!

Make your way through the maze, picking up every lettered ball as you go. Place those letters in the empty circles and see if you can unscramble them to spell out an important tip!

106   Answer on page 141.

Riddle in the Middle

Use the clues to complete the 5-letter answers, starting at the top and working your way down. When finished, read the letters in the squares with the thick boxes, from top to bottom, to reveal the answer to the riddle below.

What is black when you buy it, red when you use it, and gray when you throw it out?

1. Breakfast meat — B _ _ _ N

2. Internet search engine — Y _ _ _ O

3. Fuzzy fruit — P _ _ _ H

4. Big — L _ _ _ E

5. Hot chocolate — C _ _ _ A

6. Side of a hill — S _ _ _ E

7. Weighing device — S _ _ _ E

8. Swelling — B _ _ _ E

Space Monkeys!

Boy, this is one busy illustration, bustling with objects beginning with the letter **B**. Can you find all 17?

 Answers on page 142.

Crosspic

Looks like someone put pictures in this puzzle where there are supposed to be words! See if you can fill in the grid by writing the word—one letter for each box—that names each of the pictures. Words run across and down.

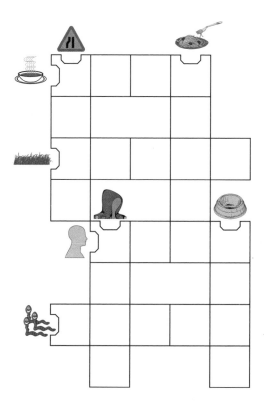

Answers on page 142.

Put on a Happy Face

ACROSS

1. A little bit of mayo, for example
4. Kids' card game
7. One of the Three Stooges
10. Abbreviation for Birmingham's state
11. Skater's surface
12. Be sick
13. Elated: 2 wds.
16. Dodge
17. Sound the horn
18. Call off
19. Arrow shooter
20. Little kiddie
21. Timid
22. "What a relief!"

25. Lightly burn
27. Mistake
29. Really happy: 3 wds.
31. Cheerleader's shout
32. "Also . . ."
33. Weep aloud
34. "I'm better than you" feeling
35. Yo-yo or Slinky
36. Historic period

DOWN
1. Computer information
2. Still breathing
3. Breakfast meat
4. Like jungle animals
5. Card with one pip
6. Like a poker in the fire: 2 wds.
7. Most important

8. Sound of a pig
9. Antlered animal
14. Girl or 19-Down
15. Explosion sound
19. Young man
20. Tonsils' location
21. Boy's name (hidden in "Psalms")
22. Son of Prince Valiant (hidden in "warning")
23. Get out of bed
24. Show respect for
25. Tear in a stocking
26. Canyon sound effect
27. Swirling water
28. Girl's name (hidden in "vampire bat")
29. Raw metal
30. Game with "Reverse" cards

Trouble at the Science Fair

There are 13 differences between these 2 illustrations.
Can you find them all?

A Wizard's Brew

As this wizard's brew bubbles over, find your way through the smoke to the finish!

Answer on page 143.

Monster Mash

Can you find the names of all the monsters below hidden in the grid? Words can be found in a straight line horizontally, vertically, or diagonally. They may read either forward or backward.

```
C Q B A D H C C I M L M E G
V H G R W E R E W O L F H V
X A E Y L F X C F K D O D C
N T M O J Y C I V E S R A W
A B W P G L B T M T Z Q Z O
M D K T I Q D B F E O S E V
E B F J F R E J M L M P B G
L W U G A M E H B X B B W I
B M Z G Y T G P T I I U R X
I G E U U N M X U T E B X R
S B V P T C C I S Y M V G N
I K O U F T V Y M M U M K T
V X J Y M F Q O J E P P R Q
N R H H I B F K X R L Q P R
I B G U U K P Z D B R R G J
```

Fitting Words

Use the clues below to complete this numberless crossword grid. The puzzle has only one solution.

1. Poisoned fruit offered to Snow White by the Evil Queen

2. Permanent mark from a healed cut

3. Takes a break from working

4. Fuzzy pool table fabric

5. Unable to bend

6. Sticky stuff used to hold gift wrap in place

7. Enemies

8. Small role in a film

9. Little rascals

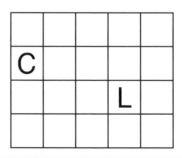

Pic-doku

The grid below is divided into 4 sections. Your job is to have each of the 4 items appear once in each section and in each row and column. Fill each square with the item's image or the letter that represents it. No item can repeat in any section, row, or column.

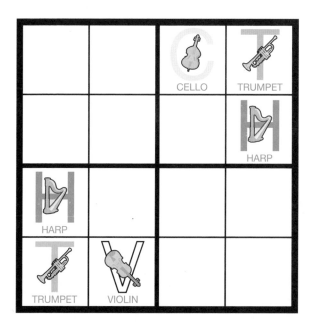

Answer on page 143.

Ride 'Em Cowboy

Every word listed is contained within the group of letters on the next page. Words can be found in a straight line horizontally, vertically, or diagonally. They may be read either forward or backward.

BANDANNA	OUTLAW
BANDIT	POSSE
BOOTS	RANCH
BRAND	RANGE
BUCKSKIN	RIFLE
CAMPFIRE	RODEO
CATTLE	RUSTLER
CHAPS	SADDLE
CHUCK WAGON	SALOON
COWBOY	SIX-SHOOTER
DEPUTY	SPURS
HERD	STAGECOACH
HORSE	STAMPEDE
LARIAT	STETSON
LASSO	TRAIL
MARSHAL	

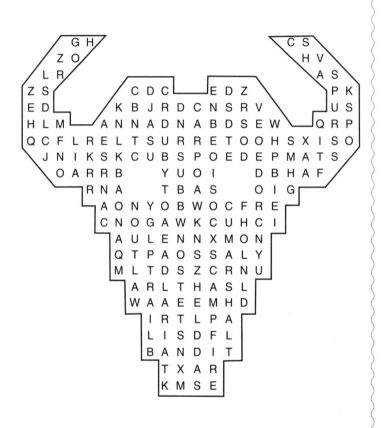

```
         G H                                    C S
         Z O                                    H V
       L R                                      A S
     Z S        C D C       E D Z               P K
     E D        K B J R D C N S R V             U S
     H L M    A N N A D N A B D S E W         Q R P
     Q C F L R E L T S U R R E T O O H S X I S O
     J N I K S K C U B S P O E D E P M A T S
       O A R R B     Y U O I     D B H A F
       R N A       T B A S     O I G
         A O N Y O B W O C F R E
         C N O G A W K C U H C I
         A U L E N N X M O N
         Q T P A O S S A L Y
         M L T D S Z C R N U
           A R L T H A S L
           W A A E E M H D
           I R T L P A
           L I S D F L
           B A N D I T
             T X A R
             K M S E
```

Luck o' the Irish!

Someone has scrambled these illustrations. See if you're lucky enough to spot all 10 changes!

121   Answers on page 144.

Country Rhymes

ACROSS

1. Boring routine
4. Boy, later on in life
7. Refuse: 2 wds
9. Ring above angels
10. Country that rhymes with "plane"
11. Seeps
12. Put in the mail
13. Country that rhymes with "peace"
14. Garden in Genesis
16. Card game with a name that you shout
17. "Nick at _____"
19. Country that rhymes with "pants"
23. One who doesn't tell the truth
27. Causing goose bumps
28. Country that rhymes with "bongo"
29. Light beside an easy chair
30. _____ for (chose)
31. Attempt
32. Keanu Reeves's role in "The Matrix"

DOWN

1. Boy's name (hidden in "country and western")
2. Come together
3. 2,000 pounds
4. Puzzle with a path
5. Boy's name (hidden in "total eclipse")
6. It really smells
7. Air leak sound
8. King Kong, for example
9. Dirt chopper
11. "Like it _____"
13. Giver of three wishes
15. Cap shaped like a cone
18. Run off to get married
19. Pool table surface
20. Backside
21. Navy's rival in sports
22. Playful bite
24. "Out of the frying pan and _____ the fire"
25. Grow older
26. Fishing pole
28. Swindle

123   Answers on page 144.

Family Ties

Divide the grid into 9 sections with each section containing 4 squares. Every section must contain one of each of the family members—mother, father, brother, and sister.

Hint: Look for places where the same family member is bunched together, and start there.

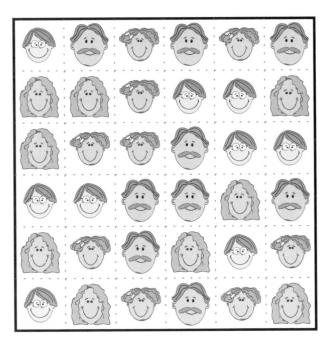

Answer on page 144.

ANSWERS

Face Off (page 6)

Word Math (page 7)

MILK + EYES − KEY = <u>M I L E S</u>

Word Ladder (page 7)

Answers may vary.
MAT, rat, rut, RUG

Decoder (page 8)

<u>B R E A T H</u>

Pic-doku (page 9)

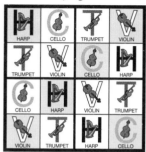

HARP	CELLO	TRUMPET	VIOLIN
TRUMPET	VIOLIN	CELLO	HARP
CELLO	HARP	VIOLIN	TRUMPET
VIOLIN	TRUMPET	HARP	CELLO

Kids' Games (pages 10-11)

```
M A D     A B C S
R O S E     L A R K
M O T H E R M A Y I
O D E ■ D U O
B E L T ■ E N D
  S I P ■ D A D
  P A T ■ M A Y O
    R O T ■ N E W
K I C K T H E C A N
I D E A     E V E R
T O E S     Y E S
```

Dozen Pawprints Blots (page 12)

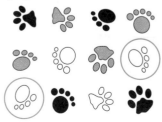

125

Answers

Silly Sundae Shop (page 13)

1. polar bear server; 2. apple instead of ice cream;
3. palm tree; 4. chicken on head; 5. jack-o'-lantern;
6. snowman; 7. fish; 8. boy has webbed feet; 9. rabbit hole in floor; 10. train; 11. fire hydrant; 12. mouse in hat; 13. woman has tail; 14. clock; 15. chair leg is a carrot; 16. ice skates

Picture-by-Number (page 14)

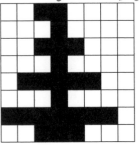

Tentacles! (page 15)

Crosspic (page 16)

Picture Crossword (page 17)

126

A Bug's Life (page 18)

Flippy Numbers (page 19)

24 × 2 = 42

↓

22 × 2 = 44

Black Diamonds (page 19)

K Is for Kite (page 20)

1. kite; 2. key; 3. kittens;
4. kimono; 5. king; 6. kilt;
7. kangaroo; 8. knot; 9. knight;
10. keg; 11. ketchup;
12. keyboard; 13. kickstand;
14. knife; 15. knitting needles;
16. koala; 17. kids

Crosspic (page 21)

Jungle Tree (pages 22-23)

Answers

Clowning Around at the Circus (page 24)

Birthday Party! (page 25)

Elliot's present was a video game (3), and Matt's present was a music CD (1). Since George didn't give Ryan a book (4), his present must have been a movie since Joe gave Ryan a book. Joe had chocolate ice cream (2), and George had strawberry ice cream (4). Since Elliot didn't have mocha ice cream (3), Elliot must have had vanilla, and Matt had mocha chip.

Matt, music CD, mocha chip; Joe, book, chocolate; Elliot, video game, vanilla; George, movie, strawberry

A Change of Seasons (page 26)

Bug Off! (page 27)

Nine Mushroom Blots (page 28)

128

Color Challenge (page 29)

A Day at the Zoo (page 30)

Monster Mash-Up! (page 31)

1. wrong calendar month;
2. Halloween is misspelled;
3. fish outside window;
4. missing eye; 5. Santa hat

Awesome Animals (pages 32-33)

1. elephant; 2. snake;
3. donkey; 4. turkey; 5. lion;
6. sheep; 7. rooster; 8. wolf;
9. parrot; 10. horse; 11. frog;
12. duck

```
M X O P G T T M Q V T K L E H
F R C P O R M G F C C Y M J N
E O X R K D L Q T S A D O R J
Y G R U G K L M V U Z O P W U
L A S S Q C S E L O R N J Y A
P Z N Q W U Q E S F N K S T B
M Z A R R D Z J T D M E E E H
R Q K T S E S N P L B Y S Y S
O P E L U T A M C P H X R O L
O D M R F H A X I Y E K O Y A
S T X L P D M V U E D E H Q F
T V O E Q K T Z Z F N W H A L
E W L G S Q Z L R O N F C S L
R E G C X Q B O I J C O N Q F
L A F Q T J G L W M H K O Y Q
```

Answers

Chain Words (page 34)

Word Math (page 34)

= APPEAR

APPLE GEAR LEG

Graveyard Shuffle (page 35)

Family Ties (page 36)

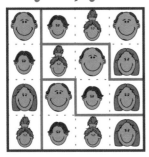

Picture-by-Number (page 37)

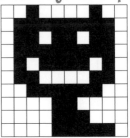

Big Top! (pages 38-39)

Space Hop (page 40)

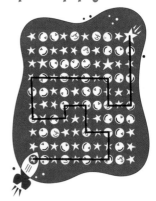

Pic-doku (page 41)

Summertime (page 42)

1. moon; 2. snowman; 3. sea monster; 4. crab missing legs; 5. winter clothes; 6. banana

Crosspic (page 43)

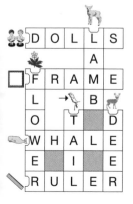

Vex-a-Gon (page 44)

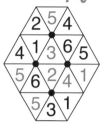

Cat Burglar (page 45)

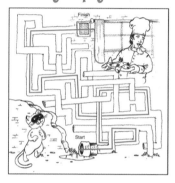

Pic-doku (page 46)

Answers

Riddle in the Middle (page 47)

A N **K** L E

C R **E** A M

L O **Y** A L

A S **H** E S

S P **O** O N

S I **L** L Y

B R **E** A D

Flower Bed (page 48)

There are 6 different flowers; this

flower () appears most; this

flower ( ) appears once.

Crosspic (page 49)

	B	R	U	S	H
		S			U
	H	E	A	R	T
	O				
	R	O	C	K	
	S		A		
	E		V		
	S	H	E	L	L

Find the Differences (pages 50–51)

Flippy Numbers (page 52)

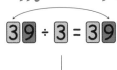

$$39 \div 3 = 39$$

$$99 \div 3 = 33$$

Word Ladder (page 52)

Answers may vary.
LOST, loot, loon, loin, COIN

Dozen Fish Blots (page 53)

132

Petting Zoo (pages 54–55)

A	Y	E			P	L	E	D
P	O	D			S	O	L	A	R
E	Y	E	S		R	O	T	A	T	E
D	O	N	K	E	Y	S		M	E	W
		I	V	E		M	A	N
	C	E	E		H	A	S
	M	A	D		B	U	Y
R	A	M		R	A	B	B	I	T	S
O	P	E	N	E	D		E	C	H	O
A	L	L	E	N			E	E	L
R	E	S	T			S	E	E

The Best Medicine
(pages 56–57)

Animal Band (page 58)

Snake Tangle (page 59)

Face Off (page 60)

Answers

Library Mix-Up (page 61)

1. closed sign; 2. bear;
3. scuba diver; 4. flowers
growing indoors; 5. turtle;
6. cat reading a book; 7. fish on
the table; 8. storybook upside
down; 9. child blindfolded;
10. monkey; 11. "men at work";
12. ladybugs; 13. atlas upside
down; 14. books hanging
upside down from shelf;
15. bird; 16. ice cream; 17. tray
of food; 18. potted flower on
girl's head; 19. owl

Dog Breeds (pages 62-63)

Disney Toons (pages 64-65)

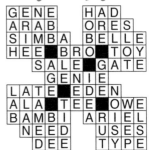

F Is for Favorites (page 66)

1. fan; 2. feather; 3. fiddle;
4. flamingo; 5. flip-flops;
6. flowers; 7. foot; 8. fox;
9. frog; 10. flute; 11. fedora;
12. ferns; 13. floor

Telescope (page 67)

GUITARANTULAWN

Save the Mayor (page 68)

Cake Connection (page 69)

School Day (pages 70-71)

```
R I A H C P B R R V C S M K U
G N J O G R E K X D N E M G W
S O E U E S J P E N C I L G L
G Y M N A S T I C S E D I D N
G A K R G N F L E H S U F M Y
Y R E D S L Y E L B A T L U P
E C E N E H I L L E B S M G W
U S Q A T S N S G T L L A W V
K P Y M O A S A H E P A T Q Q
K A U K N R P C S P K I H H R
D N I U V T H T H R F C B A T
B I R M U S I C H O N O O L R
B S T N Q R I L D G O S O L O
E H T R A H C N Z G I L K X C
I F F I U F T B K F F L O O R
```

Picture-by-Number (page 72)

Crosspic (page 73)

B	•	D	O	T
A		I		O
B	U	N	N	Y
I		O		S
E		S		
S	C	A	R	F
		U		O
J	A	R		X

Answers

Bonnie's Birthday Bash! (page 74)

Pasta Party (page 75)

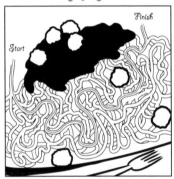

Pic-doku (page 76)

Word Math (page 77)

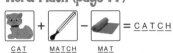

CAT   MATCH   MAT

Flower Growth (page 77)

Dig It! (pages 78-79)

Answers

Fitting Words (page 80)

S	L	A	S	H
C	A	N	O	E
A	C	T	O	R
T	E	S	T	S

Something's Not Right! (page 81)

Abracadabra! (page 82)

Damsel in Distress (page 83)

Picture-by-Number (page 84)

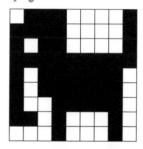

Pic-doku (page 85)

137

Answers

Chain Words (page 86)

Word Math (page 86)

Oodles of Octopi (page 87)

Jumbled Up (page 88)

Black Diamonds (page 88)

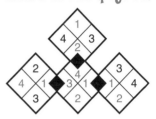

Face Off (page 89)

Circus Animals (pages 90-91)

```
    M A S     I D A
    D A R T   D O G S
T I G E R   L E R O Y
A M I ■ I C E ■ E R A
R E C I P E ■ S E E M
    S E A L S
A R E A ■ S I S T E R
W E D ■ L E G ■ A L A
L A D L E   H O R S E
  L I O N   T I D E
    E N D   S L Y
```

138

Bert's Bicycles (page 92)

Alien Invasion! (page 93)

1. 6 arms; 2. antennas; 3. spots;
4. 3 eyes; 5. dark oval eyes;
6. space helmet

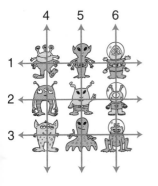

Go Fish! (pages 94-95)

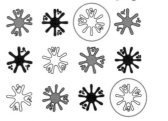

Dozen Stars Blots (page 96)

On the Job (page 97)

Answers

Crosspic (page 98)

```
      P  O  I  N  T
      I     C     A
      I     E     G
      S  O  C  K  P
         R     ▓  P
      W  H  E  E  L
      E     A     U
      B     M     M
```

Flower Fiesta! (page 99)

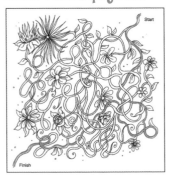

Start

Finish

What You Want on a Picnic (pages 100–101)

```
S O D A     A H A
A M I D     S O L E S
L I M A S   A T I L T
  T E M P O ■ D E F Y
      U N I O N
    B R I N G
    P U T O N
A F A R ■ N I N E S
B I N G O   E A V E S
E N D E D   L E N S
A R E       A N T S
```

Fitting Words (page 102)

```
W H A L E
R E L A Y
E R A S E
N E S T S
```

Pic-doku (page 103)

LEOPARD	BUNNY	MONKEY	HIPPO
MONKEY	HIPPO	LEOPARD	BUNNY
HIPPO	MONKEY	BUNNY	LEOPARD
BUNNY	LEOPARD	HIPPO	MONKEY

140

Knight-ly Dinner (page 104)

1. television; 2. rocket ship;
3. car; 4. sunglasses; 5. can of
cola; 6. wristwatch; 7. drinking
straw; 8. cell phone

Great Lesson! (page 106)

WATCH

THE BALL

Theme Park (page 105)

```
      P A I N T
      C R A Y O N S
  P A S T E L S
    E A S E L
    G L U E
    P A P E R
        P E N C I L
      C L A Y
      S C I S S O R S
M A R K E R
  B R U S H
```

Riddle in the Middle (page 107)

B A C O N

Y A H O O

P E A C H

L A R G E

C O C O A

S L O P E

S C A L E

B U L G E

141

Answers

Space Monkeys! (page 108)

Put on a Happy Face (pages 110–111)

D	A	B		W	A	R		M	O	E
A	L	A			I	C	E		A	I	L
T	I	C	K	L	E	D	P	I	N	K
A	V	O	I	D		█	H	O	N	K
	E	N	D		█	B	O	W		
			T	O	T					
	S	H	Y		█	A	A	H	
	S	E	A	R		█	E	R	R	O	R
O	N	C	L	O	U	D	N	I	N	E
R	A	H		A	N	D		S	O	B
E	G	O		T	O	Y		E	R	A

Trouble at the Science Fair (pages 112–113)

Crosspic (page 109)

142

Answers

A Wizard's Brew (page 114)

Monster Mash (page 115)

Fitting Words (page 116)

Pic-doku (page 117)

Ride 'Em Cowboy! (pages 118–119)

143

Answers

Luck o' the Irish!
(pages 120-121)

Country Rhymes
(pages 122-123)

Family Ties (page 124)

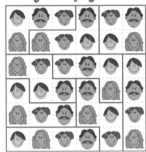